SCHONELL'S ESSENTIAL
SPELLING LIST

Workbook 1

FRED J SCHONELL

team	slave	front	shape
steam	shave	month	treat
scream	grave	Monday	won
gleam	cape	ton	wonder

☆ Learn the words, then use them to do the exercises.

☆ **WORD MAKER** Use words from the list to complete the words below.

1 sl*a ve*   (a person owned by another)

2 gr*ave*   (a burial place)

3 sh*a ve*   (to scrape off hair with a razor)

4 gl*ea*m   (a small beam of light)

5 tre*a*t   (a gift or feast paid for by another)

6 fr*o*nt   (a position directly ahead)

7 m*on*th   (one of the twelve divisions of the year)

8 w*o*nder   (a feeling of surprise)

9 M*o*nday   (a day of the week)

☆ **WORD PUZZLE** Use the word 'wonder' to help form six words from the list.

¹w	i	n			succeeded
² o	n				measurement of weight
³M	o	n	t	h	division of the year
⁴m o	n	d	a	y	day of the week
⁵R a	p	e			a short cloak
⁶S	c	r	e	a	m a loud yell

☆ **WORD HUNT** Which words in the list have these smaller words inside them?

1 ape *cape*   and   *shape*

2 tea *team*   and   *steam*

☆ **WORD MATCH** Find words in the list which mean the same as these words.

1 yell   *scream*   3 gained   *won*

2 shine   *gleam*

paying	upper	rode	pray
playing	sudden	globe	plays
saying	suffer	joke	flutter
staying	offer	poker	close

☆ Learn the words, then use them to do the exercises.

☆ **WORD PUZZLE**   Use words from the list to complete the puzzle.

Clues down

1 funny story
2 beg or implore
5 quick flapping motion
6 drove a horse or bicycle
8 dramatic performances
10 a sphere

Clues across

2 taking part in a game
3 card game
4 to present
7 higher
9 proverb
11 to shut
12 to feel pain

☆ **WORD HUNT**   Which words in the list have these smaller words inside them?

1 off _____ Of _____
2 lose _____ so _____
3 ray _____ Pray _____
4 lobe _____ be _____
5 rod _____ do _____

6 utter _____ flutter _____
7 den _____ sudden _____
8 lays _____ plays _____
9 stay _____ staying _____

vain	thunder	soil	shock
plain	peal	spoil	burst
obtain	stuck	noise	moment
faint	struck	swift	rainbow

☆ Learn the words, then use them to do the exercises.

☆ **WORD HUNT** Fill the gaps in the story with words from the list.

What a (1) _noise_ the (2) ~~first~~ _peal_ of (3) _thunder_

made! It gave me such a (4) _shock_ that I thought I would

(5) _faint_. I thought I would be (6) _struck_ by lightning.

A (7) _moment_ later, however, a (8) _rainbow_ appeared in the sky.

It was (9) _plain_ that the storm was over.

☆ **EXPLANATIONS** Complete these sentences with words from the list.

1 Another word for 'quick' is _swift_.

2 Another word for 'hit' is _struck_.

3 Another word for 'glued' is _stuck_.

☆ **MINI PUZZLE** Use the word 'spoil' to help form five words from the list.

¹b	a	r	s	t
	²s	p	o	i	l
		³o	b	t	a	i	n
⁴v	a	i	n
⁵s	o	i	l

to explode
to damage
to get
having a high opinion of oneself
earth

☆ **WORD MATCH** Find words in the list which mean the same as these words.

1 quick _swift_

2 hit _struck_

3 proud _vain_

pocket	needle	light	stockings
silver	button	sight	high
money	sew	might	sigh
honey	print	fight	fright

☆ Learn the words, then use them to do the exercises.

☆ **WORD HUNT**   Complete these sentences with words from the list.

1 The only _money_ he had in his _Pocke_ was a _Silver_ coin.

2 I'll get a _needle_ and _Sow_ that _button_ on.

3 My _Sight_ is getting worse. I can't read the small _Print_.

4 He had a _High_ opinion of himself.

5 She gave a _Sigh_ of relief when she heard the news.

6 My sister has a sweet tooth. She loves _honey_.

7 I bought my friend a pair of _Stocking_ for her birthday.

☆ **WORD HUNT**   Which words in the list have these smaller words inside them?

1 rig _Sight_   4 need _needle_

2 fig _High_   5 sigh _Sight_

3 king _Sigh_   6 ton _button_

☆ **EXPLANATIONS**   Complete these sentences with words from the list.

1 Another word for 'vision' is _Sight_.

2 Another word for 'strength' is _might_.

3 Another word for 'combat' is _____.

4 Another word for 'fear' is _fright_.

5 Another word for 'radiance' is _____.

robber	real	proud	bear
ladder	deal	pride	wear
bottom	steal	spite	tear
rabbit	leap	rage	pear

☆ Learn the words, then use them to do the exercises.

☆ **WORD PUZZLE**   Use words from the list to complete the puzzle.

Clues down

1 jump
2 do business
3 long-eared mammal
4 a thief

Clues across

1 a framework of steps
5 the lowest part
6 ill will
7 to have a garment on

☆ **WORD HUNT**   Complete these sentences with words from the list. All the words have 'ear' inside them.

1 The hunter shot the great _____.

2 I must mend the _____ in my dress.

3 A juicy _____ fell off the tree.

4 My mother told me to _____ the blue dress.

☆ **WORD MATCH**   Find words in the list which mean the same as these words.

1 genuine _____

2 arrogance _____

3 rob _____

4 arrogant _____

5 anger _____

singing	begin	prince	lord
bringing	began	princess	state
blowing	begun	crown	gain
feeling	music	crowd	main

☆ Learn the words, then use them to do the exercises.

☆ **WORD PUZZLE**   Use the word 'singing' to help form seven words from the list.

P	R	I	N	C	E	S	S	daughter of a king
			m	u	s	i	C	melodious sounds
		C	R	O	w	n		royal head dress
				B	E	g	I	N	start
				P	R	i	N	C	E	son of a king
						n		principal
					g	A	I	N	to win

☆ **WORD HUNT**   Which words in the list have these smaller words inside them?

1 ring _____   5 ate _____

2 low _____   6 or _____

3 gun _____   7 own _____

4 eel _____   8 us _____

☆ **EXPLANATIONS**   Complete these sentences with words from the list.

1 The word which means 'started' is _____.

2 The word which means 'a large group of people' is _____.

3 The word which means 'nation' is _____.

4 Another word for 'win' is _____.

5 Another word for 'melody' is _____.

sow	turnip	vine	depart
grain	straw	wine	travel
wheat	claw	grape	return
pea	drawing	field	remain

☆ Learn the words, then use them to do the exercises.

☆ **WORD PUZZLE**   Use the word 'drawing' to help form seven words from the list.

1 d	a meadow
2 r	a root vegetable
3 a	a small green vegetable
4 w	to scatter seed
5 i	plant on which grapes grow
6 n	drink made from grapes
7 g	the seed of a cereal plant

☆ **WORD HUNT**   Which words in the list have these smaller words inside them?

1   rain _____

2   wing _____

3   main _____

4   ape _____

5   nip _____

6   law _____

7   eat _____

8   part _____

9   rave _____

10   raw _____

11   win _____

☆ **WORD MAKER**   Use words from the list to complete the words below.

1   _ _ aw   (a bird's toe nail)

2   _ _ _ aw   (dried stems of cereals)

3   _ _ aw _ _ _   (a sketch)

4   re _ _ _ _ _   (to come back)

5   re _ _ _ _ _   (to stay)

animal	port	prison	lion
donkey	tide	pardon	rude
monkey	shore	forgive	swan
monkeys	coast	punish	polite

☆ Learn the words, then use them to do the exercises.

☆ **WORD PUZZLE**   Use the word 'animal' to help form six words from the list.

1 **a**	to forgive
2 **n**	ass
3 **i**	ebb or flow of the sea
4 **m**	long tailed animal
5 **a**	a graceful bird
6 **l**	King of the animals

☆ **EXPLANATIONS**   Complete these sentences with words from the list.

1 The word which means the same as 'pardon' is _____.

2 Another word for 'gaol' is _____.

3 The word which means 'well mannered' is _____.

4 Two other words for 'seaside' are _____ and _____.

5 A word which means 'bad mannered' is _____.

☆ **WORD HUNT**   Which words in the list have these smaller words inside them?

1 an _____ and _____

2 is _____ and _____

3 or _____, _____ and _____

☆ **WORD HUNT**   Complete these sentences with words from the list.

1 The criminal was sent to _____ for two years.

2 A _____ is a graceful bird.

3 There were a lot of boats in the _____.

gather	owl	arrow	yellow
rather	growl	narrow	pillow
path	chicken	sorrow	understand
enter	crust	borrow	understood

☆ Learn the words, then use them to do the exercises.

☆ **WORD MAKER**   Use words from the list to complete the words below.

1 ow __   (bird of prey)

2 _ _ _ ow   (weapon shot from a bow)

3 _ _ ow __   (gruff, angry sound)

4 _ _ _ _ ow   (small in breadth)

5 _ _ _ _ ow   (a bright colour)

6 _ _ _ _ ow   (obtain something on loan)

7 _ _ _ _ ow   (cushion for the head in bed)

8 _ _ _ _ ow   (sadness)

☆ **WORD PUZZLE**   Use the word 'rather' to help form six words from the list.

1		r				
2		a				
3		t				
4		h				
5		e				
6		r				

hard outer covering

collect

narrow track

domestic fowl

come in

knew the meaning of

☆ **WORD HUNT**   Which words in the list have these smaller words inside them?

1 at _____, _____ and _____

2 stand _____

3 rust _____

shallow	anger	pale	wade
stream	hunger	shake	trade
moss	hungry	snake	sash
carpet	drank	danger	splash

☆ Learn the words, then use them to do the exercises.

☆ **WORD PUZZLE**   Use words from the list to complete the puzzle.

Clues down

2 tremble
3 rage
4 exchange one thing for another
5 walk in water
7 belt or waist band

Clues across

1 plant which grows on moist ground
6 emptiness through lack of food
8 had a drink

☆ **WORD HUNT**   Complete these sentences with words from the list.

1 The word which is made up of two three-letter words is _____.

2 If you have not eaten all day, you will be _____.

3 If you wade into a _____ and slip, you may make a _____.

4 A _____ is a kind of reptile.

☆ **OPPOSITES**   Find words in the list which mean the opposite of these words.

1 safety _____

2 deep _____

3 dark _____

March	**form**	**large**	**someone**
April	**thorn**	**charge**	**something**
May	**marble**	**strange**	**sometimes**
trust	**tumble**	**stranger**	**stable**

☆ Learn the words, then use them to do the exercises.

☆ **WORD PUZZLE**   Use the word 'sometimes' to help form nine words from the list.

1 s _ _ _ _ _	horse's shed
2 o _ _ _ _ _	some person
3 m _ _	fall
4 e _ _ _ _ _	unknown object
5 t _ _ _	rely on
6 i _ _	fourth month of the year
7 m _ _ _	small glass or stone ball
8 e _ _ _ _	set a price
9 s _ _ _ _ _	unusual

☆ **WORD HUNT**   Complete these sentences with words from the list.

1 The word with the most vowels is _____.

2 The shortest word in the list is _____.

3 Three months are named in the list. The only letter common to all is _.

4 Another word for 'big' is _____.

☆ **WORD HUNT**   Which words in the list have these smaller words inside them?

1 or   _____ and _____

2 ranger   _____

3 arch   _____

sort	Sunday	dusty	anybody
sport	Thursday	stormy	nobody
handle	Friday	frosty	happen
candle	unless	cloudy	cannot

☆ Learn the words, then use them to do the exercises.

☆ **WEATHER WORDS**   Which words describe weather which is

1 dry?   _____

2 cold?   _____

3 dull?   _____

4 wet and windy _____

☆ **WORD HUNT**   Complete these sentences with words from the list.

1 The word containing the most consonants is _____.

2 The word where the letter 's' appears most often is _____.

3 The word where the letter 'p' appears most often is _____.

4 The word where the letter 'y' appears most often is _____.

5 The word where the letter 'o' appears most often is _____.

6 The day before Saturday is _____.

7 The day after Saturday is _____.

8 The shortest word ending in 'y' is _____.

9 The longest word ending in 'y' is _____.

10 The only word ending in 'n' is _____.

☆ **WORD HUNT**   Which words in the list have these smaller words inside them?

1 or   _____, _____ and _____

2 less   _____

3 pen   _____

4 hand _____

5 can   _____

lamb	sleepy	stove	climb
comb	dirty	glove	steady
crumb	busy	cover	none
thumb	lucky	shelter	become

☆ Learn the words, then use them to do the exercises.

☆ **WORD HUNT**   Which words in the list have these smaller words inside them?

1 rum _____

2 hum _____

3 bus _____

4 love _____

5 one _____

6 come _____

7 over _____

8 luck _____

9 he _____

10 tea _____

☆ **OPPOSITES**   Find words in the list which mean the opposite of these words.

1 clean _____

2 idle _____

3 wakeful _____

4 unfortunate _____

8 wobbly _____

9 descend _____

☆ **WORD HUNT**

1 Which five words in the list end with a silent 'b'?

_____; _____; _____;

_____; _____.

2 Which four words end with a silent 'e'?

_____; _____;

_____; _____.

☆ **WORD HUNT**   Complete these sentences with words from the list.

1 I'm not _____. I never seem to win anything.

2 We liked the cake so much that we didn't even leave a _____ on our plates.

3 It was raining heavily but we couldn't find any _____.

brain	**power**	**roll**	**heart**
brow	**shower**	**rolled**	**act**
chest	**tower**	**rolling**	**cottage**
cheek	**towel**	**pulled**	**pudding**

☆ Learn the words, then use them to do the exercises.

☆ **WORD MAKER**   Use words from the list to complete the words below.

1 _ _ ow   (forehead)

2 _ ow _ _   (strength or might)

3 _ ow _ _   (cloth for drying the body)

4 _ ow _ _   (tall structure)

5 _ _ ow _ _   (brief period of rain)

6 _ _ ll   (rotate)

7 _ _ ll _ _   (rotated)

8 _ _ ll _ _   (tugged)

9 _ _ ll _ _ _   (turning over and over)

☆ **WORD PUZZLE**   Use the word 'cottage' to help form seven words from the list.

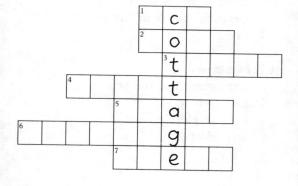

take part in a play

to turn over

a tall building

large, sturdy box

part of the body

cooked dessert

either side of the face

☆ **WORD HUNT**   Complete these sentences with words from the list.

1 'You've got a good _____,' the teacher said, 'but you don't work hard

enough.'

2 The gardener had a small _____ in the grounds of the big house.

3 I was caught in a _____ and got wet to the skin.

match	June	picking	fetch
catch	July	picked	ditch
patch	September	learned	snatch
watch	November	reached	everyone

☆ Learn the words, then use them to do the exercises.

☆ **WORD MAKER** Use words from the list to complete the words below.

1 _ _ _ tch (seize suddenly)

2 _ _ tch (capture after a chase)

3 _ _ tch (contest or game)

4 _ _ tch (material to mend clothing)

5 _ _ tch (observe closely)

6 _ _ tch (bring)

7 _ _ tch (get rid of something)

☆ **WORD PUZZLE** Use words from the list to complete the puzzle.

Clues down

1 seventh month of the year
2 eleventh month of the year
3 bring

Clues across

1 sixth month of the year
4 each person
5 observe closely
6 arrived at

☆ **WORD HUNT** Which words in the list have these smaller words inside them?

1 ember _____ and _____

2 pick _____ and _____

3 earn _____

care	infant	tender	purse
careless	darling	gentle	nurse
useless	cradle	weak	fur
useful	young	dull	beak

☆ Learn the words, then use them to do the exercises.

☆ **WORD PUZZLE**   Use the word 'darling' to help form seven words from the list.

			d			
		a				
		r				
		l				
		i				
		n				
		g				

a baby's bed

a bird's jaw

a small money bag

beloved

very young child

one who tends the sick

having a mild nature

☆ **OPPOSITES**   Find words in the list which mean the opposite of these words.

1 strong _____

2 bright _____

3 harsh _____

4 old _____

5 useful _____

6 careful _____

☆ **WORD MATCH**   Find words in the list which mean the same as these words.

1 beloved _____

2 youthful _____

3 feeble _____

4 tedious _____

☆ **WORD HUNT**   Complete these sentences with words from the list.

1 The baby was asleep in her _____.

2 The _____ put a bandage on my finger.

3 A _____ coat is very expensive.

4 The meat is very _____.

hammer	too	lunch	blood
bench	tool	buy	goose
blade	stool	beef	geese
wire	fool	cloth	cheese

☆ Learn the words, then use them to do the exercises.

☆ **WORD PUZZLE**   Use words from the list to complete the puzzle.

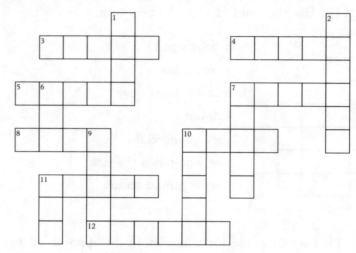

Clues down

1 implement
2 solid food made from milk
6 also
7 plural of 7 across
9 midday meal
10 cutting edge of a weapon
11 purchase

Clues across

3 red fluid in the veins
4 material
5 small seat
7 a web-footed bird
8 simpleton
10 flesh of the cow
11 work table
12 tool for driving in nails

☆ **WORD HUNT**   Complete these sentences with words from the list.

1 I need a _____ to clean the floor.

2 My mother bought two fat _____ for our dinner.

3 Tom cut his finger with a _____ and he got _____ all

over his trousers.

4 Can you show me how to _____ this plug?

change	break	brighter	cooler
changed	broke	brightest	deeper
taken	broken	safer	finer
eaten	stole	safest	miner

☆ Learn the words, then use them to do the exercises.

☆ **WORD PUZZLE**   Use the word 'brightest' to help form nine words from the list.

	b			
	r			
	i	miner		
change		g		
	h	changed		
	t			
	e			
	s			
	t			

fractured

giving more light

one who works in a mine

alter

altered

gained possession of

cracked

took unlawfully

consumed

☆ **WORD HUNT**   Complete these sentences with words from the list.

1 The word in which 'o' appears most often is ___cooler___.

2 The word with the most consonants is ___brightest___.

3 The word in which 'e' appears most often is ___deeper___.

4 The words which have 'safe' inside them are ___safer___ and ___safest___.

5 The words which have 'right' inside them are ___brighter___ and ___brightest___.

☆ **OPPOSITES**   Find words in the list which mean the opposite of these words.

1 coarser _____

2 repair _____

3 duller _____

4 hotter _____

5 repaired _____

6 shallower _____

7 given _____

8 more dangerous _____

hiding	skate	chief	should
shining	skating	thief	cheer
smiling	darkness	grief	quickly
hoping	illness	burnt	nearly

☆ Learn the words, then use them to do the exercises.

☆ **WORD PUZZLE**   Use words from the list to complete the puzzle.

Clues down

2 one who steals
4 absence of light
5 deep sorrow
6 gleaming
7 looking amused
8 applaud with shouts
10 large flat fish

Clues across

1 consumed by fire
3 concealing
8 head of tribe
9 disease
11 slide smoothly over a surface

☆ **WORD MATCH**   Find words in the list which mean the same as these words.

1 almost _____

2 rapidly _____

3 sorrow _____

4 sickness _____

5 applaud _____

6 charred _____

☆ **WORD HUNT**   Complete these sentences with words from the list.

1 You really _____ give up smoking. It is bad for you.

2 The sun was _____ when I left the house.

3 The _____ got away with all the jewellery.

write	prove	gray	remark
writing	move	clay	repair
wrote	remove	poem	Easter
wrap	repeat	poet	Christmas

☆ Learn the words, then use them to do the exercises.

☆ **WORD PUZZLES**   Use the words 'remove' and 'Easter' to help form twelve words from the list.

r	the work of a writer
e	do something again
m	be in motion
o	composition in verse
v	show to be true
e	describe ideas with pen and paper

E	take away
a	mend
s	a time for presents
t	one who writes verse
e	corresponded
r	to cover with paper or cloth

☆ **WORD HUNT**   Which words in the list have these smaller words inside them?

1 ark _____

2 as _____

3 lay _____

4 ray _____

5 peat _____

6 rot _____

☆ **WORD HUNT**   Complete these sentences with words from the list.

1 I must _____ the present in paper.

2 Please _____ your shoes before you come into the house.

3 Can you _____ the question, please?

aloud	**coal**	**yesterday**	**roam**
around	**roast**	**afternoon**	**grandmother**
alike	**cloak**	**however**	**above**
afraid	**float**	**breakfast**	**usual**

☆ Learn the words, then use them to do the exercises.

☆ **WORD PUZZLE** Use words from the list to complete the puzzle.

Clues down

1 mother of one's parent
2 in a spoken voice
3 on all sides of
4 similar
5 wander
7 an outer garment

Clues across

3 on top of
4 frightened
6 normal
8 the day before today

☆ **WORD MIX-UP!** The syllables of these words have got mixed up. Rearrange them to make three words from the list.

noonbreak   howfast   everafter

Write your own words below.

1 _____   2 _____   3 _____

☆ **WORD MAKER** Use words from the list to complete the words below.

1 _ oa _   (to wander)

2 _ oa _   (a black rock)

3 _ _ oa _   (a garment worn around the shoulders)

4 _ _ oa _   (to rest in air or liquid)

branch	classes	together	inches
branches	glasses	towards	worth
peach	order	afterwards	starve
peaches	border	forward	husband

☆ Learn the words, then use them to do the exercises.

☆ **WORD PUZZLE**   Use words from the list to complete the puzzle.

Clues down

2 later
3 moving ahead
4 dividing line
5 spectacles
8 twelfths of a foot
9 value
11 limbs of a tree

Clues across

1 deprive of food
6 in the direction of
7 divisions
10 command
11 singular of 11 down
12 woman's partner in marriage
13 in union with each other
14 soft, juicy fruits

☆ **MORE THAN ONE**   Write the plural of these words.

1 branch _____

2 peach _____

3 inch _____

4 glass _____

5 class _____

price	pepper	visit	bitter
twice	copper	fir	silly
since	cuff	birth	stiff
fence	stuff	birthday	hurry

☆ Learn the words, then use them to do the exercises.

☆ **WORD PUZZLE** Use words from the list to complete the puzzle.

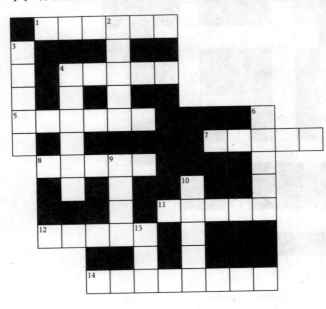

Clues down

2 on two occasions
3 because
4 a hot spice
6 hasten
9 part of sleeve nearest the hand
10 the act of being born
13 a tree with needles and cones

Clues across

1 having a harsh taste
4 cost
5 reddish metal
7 fill completely
8 fight with swords
11 foolish
12 rigid
14 anniversary of one's birth

☆ **OPPOSITES** Find words in the list which mean the opposite of these words.

1 sensible _____

2 dawdle _____

3 loose _____

5 sweet _____

☆ **WORD HUNT** Complete these sentences with words from the list.

1 The word in which 't' occurs most often is _____.

2 The word in which 'p' occurs most often is _____.

3 The word 'sit' is inside _____.

provide	dwell	friend	finger
pretend	present	quiet	flesh
forest	lemon	boxes	wool
track	sugar	dishes	bloom

☆ Learn the words, then use them to do the exercises.

☆ **WORD PUZZLE**   Use words from the list to complete the puzzle.

Clues down

2 sheep's coat
3 yellow, oval fruit
4 containers, usually lidded
5 make believe
6 supply
7 a sweetening agent
9 trail or path

Clues across

1 reside
4 flower
8 gift
10 without noise
11 containers for holding food

☆ **EXPLANATIONS**   Complete these sentences with words from the list.

1 Another word for 'companion' is _____.

2 A _____ is a bitter fruit.

3 Another word for 'meat' is _____.

4 A _____ is a large area covered with trees.

5 A _____ is one of the members of the hand.

cling	serve	four	eleven
strip	person	fourth	simple
pint	term	fifth	twelve
gift	upset	tenth	hundred

☆ Learn the words, then use them to do the exercises.

☆ **WORD MAKER**   Use words from the list to complete the words below.

1   _ _ _ _ th   (4th)

2   _ _ _ th   (5th)

3   _ _ _ th   (10th)

☆ **WORD PUZZLE**   Use the word 'eleven' to help form six words from the list.

a human being

hold on to something desperately

limited period of time

dozen

perform a duty

ten tens

☆ **WORD HUNT**   Complete these sentences with words from the list.

1   Four and seven make _____.

2   Two and two make _____.

3   A _____ is a measure of liquid.

4   I bought my friend a _____ for her birthday.

5   My mother was _____ when I told her the bad news.

☆ **WORD MATCH**   Find words in the list which mean the same as these words.

1   undress _____

2   overturn _____

3   easy _____

4   present _____

daisy	wise	earn	voice
daisies	spider	earth	bravely
lily	soap	grace	invite
lilies	soak	space	chance

☆ Learn the words, then use them to do the exercises.

☆ **WORD MAKER**   Use words from the list to complete the words below.

1 _ _ _ ce   (used in speaking)

2 _ _ _ ce   (beauty of movement)

3 _ _ _ ce   (a blank area)

4 _ _ _ _ ce   (opportunity)

5 ea _ _   (to gain)

6 ea _ _ _   (soil)

☆ **WORD HUNT**   Complete these sentences with words from the list.

1 The two plural words are _____ and _____ .

2 The word 'rave' is inside _____ .

3 The word 'it' is inside _____ .

4 The word 'ice' is inside _____ .

5 The word 'so' is inside _____ and _____ .

☆ **WORD PUZZLE**   Use the word 'daisies' to help form seven words from the list.

a small wild flower

to leave in water

a tall white flower

a cleaning substance

showing good judgement

to gain

an eight-legged insect

steep	thirteen	thirty	thousand
steel	fourteen	twenty	creeping
wheel	fifteen	fifty	indeed
deed	sixteen	sixty	between

☆ Learn the words, then use them to do the exercises.

☆ **NUMBER WORDS**   Use number words from the list.

(a) 30 _____

(b) 13 _____

(c) 50 _____

(d) 16 _____

(e) 14 _____

(f) 20 _____

(g) 60 _____

(h) 15 _____

☆ **WORD MAKER**   Use words from the list to complete the words below.

1 _ _ ee _   (disc joined to a hub by spokes)

2 _ _ _ _ ee _   (in combination, together)

3 _ _ ee _   (to soak)

4 _ _ ee _ _ _ _   (crawling)

5 _ ee _   (an act)

6 _ _ _ ee _   (really)

☆ **WORD HUNT**   Complete these sentences with words from the list.

1 The word with the most vowels is _____.

2 The word in which 'e' occurs most often is _____.

3 The word 'sand' is inside _____.

4 The word 'eel' is inside _____ and _____.

5 Another word for 'act' is _____.

6 Ten times one hundred is a _____.

7 Eight and eight are _____.

8 A half of forty is _____.

half	halves	flew	wolf
calf	leaves	threw	themselves
shelf	thieves	crew	grind
loaf	loaves	chew	thrown

☆ Learn the words, then use them to do the exercises.

☆ **WORD PUZZLE**   Use the word 'thieves' to help form seven words from the list.

```
1  t  .
2  h
3  i
4  e
5  v
6  e
7  s
```

cast

one of two equal parts of a whole

to reduce to small particles by pounding

the men who man a ship

the plural of leaf

ledge

the plural of half

☆ **MORE THAN ONE**   Write the plural of these words.

1 loaf _____   4 leaf _____

2 thief _____   5 himself _____

3 half _____

☆ **WORD HUNT**   Complete these sentences with words from the list.

1 The meat was tough and difficult to _____.

2 When Concord _____ over, it made a terrific noise.

3 I can't reach the top _____ of my bookcase. It's too high.

4 The car hit the bicycle and the cyclist was _____ to the ground.

5 The ship's _____ went ashore.

6 I bought a _____ of bread in the shop.

7 My friends enjoyed _____ at the fair.

8 The _____ escaped with the money.

knee	knife	mail	flock
kneel	knives	rail	finish
knot	wives	snail	tie
knock	fixed	jail	tied

☆ Learn the words, then use them to do the exercises.

☆ **WORD PUZZLE**   Use words from the list to complete the puzzle.

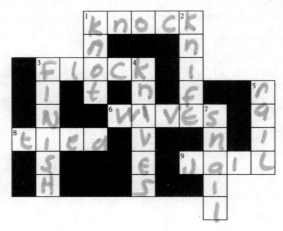

Clues down

1 a fastening
2 a cutting instrument
3 end
4 plural of 2 down
5 post
7 slow creature with coiled shell

Clues across

1 strike
3 group of animals of one kind
6 married women
8 fastened
9 prison

☆ **WORD HUNT**   Complete these sentences with words from the list.

1 My father always travels by British _____.

2 I hurt my _____ playing football yesterday.

3 My friend _____ my bicycle for me this morning.

☆ **PAIRS**   Which words from the list would you choose to go with these words?

1 husbands and _____

2 a shirt and _____

3 a _____ and fork

raise	cure	capture	dread
raised	sure	defend	deaf
trunk	pure	dying	heaven
strike	picture	lying	paid

☆ Learn the words, then use them to do the exercises.

☆ **WORD PUZZLE**   Use words from the list to complete the puzzle.

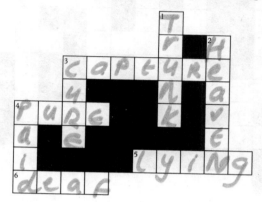

Clues down
1 main stem of a tree
2 state of joy
3 heal
4 discharged a debt

Clues across
3 gain control over
4 wholesome
5 not telling the truth
6 unable to hear

☆ **OPPOSITES**   Find words in the list which mean the opposite of these words.

1 lower _____highter_____

2 uncertain _____certain_____

3 attack _____defend_____

4 lowered _____highered_____

☆ **WORD MATCH**   Find words in the list which mean the same as these words.

1 hit _____strike_____

2 fear _____dread_____

3 illustration _____

4 expiring _____

5 certain _____

6 lift _____

built	battle	kettle	rate
build	rattle	bottle	flame
building	cattle	cork	frame
content	tired	sore	scrape

☆ Learn the words, then use them to do the exercises.

☆ **WORD PUZZLE** Use words from the list to complete the puzzle.

Clues down

1 remove by rubbing
2 a baby's toy
3 constructed
4 container for boiling water
5 peace of mind
8 construct
9 weary
10 price or charge

Clues across

1 painfully tender
6 cows
7 a stopper for bottles
8 vessel for liquids
11 fiery glow
12 an enclosing border
13 fight between large armed forces

☆ **WORD HUNT** Which words in the list have these smaller words inside them?

1 ate _____

2 red _____

3 din _____

☆ **WORD HUNT** Complete these sentences with words from the list.

1 The _____ were grazing in the field.

2 I bought a _____ for my baby sister.

3 Tom went to bed because he was _____.

swimming	toe	trying	shy
slipped	scout	flying	spy
matter	shout	army	butterfly
manner	axe	rank	answer

☆ Learn the words, then use them to do the exercises.

☆ **WORD PUZZLE**   Use words from the list to complete the puzzle.

Clues down

1 reply
2 propelling oneself in water
3 stroke used in 2 down
6 nation's soldiers
10 timid
11 a line or row

Clues across

2 one sent ahead to gain information
4 loud cry
5 lost balance and slid
6 hatchet
7 finger of the foot
8 bearing or behaviour
9 substance or material
10 one who keeps secret watch on others
12 moving through the air
13 attempting

☆ **WORD MATCH**   Find words in the list which mean the same as these words.

1 timid _____

2 yell _____

3 substance _____

4 reply _____

5 behaviour _____

heavy	easier	cause	arch
heavier	easiest	because	starch
heaviest	easily	instant	touch
war	merrily	shadow	being

☆ Learn the words, then use them to do the exercises.

☆ **WORD PUZZLE** Use the word 'heaviest' to help form eight words from the list.

1 h	used to stiffen cloth
2 e	joyfully
3 a	curved structure over opening
4 v	more weighty
5 i	living person
6 e	simplest
7 s	for
8 t	come in contact with

☆ **WORD HUNT** Fill in the gaps with words from the list.

Having lost two stones, Mary is but a (1) _____ of her former self.

Even so, she is still (2) _____ at 12 stone. Jane, at 12½ stone,

is even (3) _____. But Joanna is the (4) _____ of all at

13 stone.

☆ **OPPOSITES** Find words in the list which mean the opposite of these words.

1 peace _____   4 light _____

2 delayed _____   5 prevent _____

3 with difficulty _____ 6 more difficult _____

☆ **WORD HUNT** Which words in the list have these smaller words inside them?

1 had _____

2 star _____

3 ant _____

4 us _____ and _____

past	copy	taste	loss
mast	pity	waste	lose
fasten	empty	haste	glory
odd	plenty	good-bye	history

☆ Learn the words, then use them to do the exercises.

☆ **WORD PUZZLE** Use words from the list to complete the puzzle.

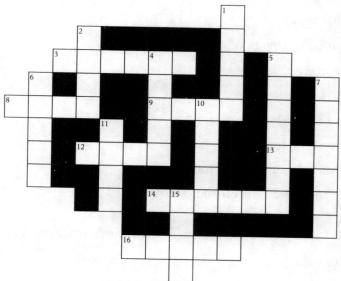

Clues down
1 pomp, splendour
2 upright spar to support sails
4 containing nothing
5 the recorded past
6 use up thoughtlessly
7 farewell
10 flavour
11 the act of losing
15 fail to win

Clues across
3 make secure
8 no longer existing
9 sympathy
12 imitate
13 peculiar
14 a great number
16 the act of hurrying

☆ **OPPOSITES** Find words in the list which mean the opposite of these words.

1 find _____

2 present _____

3 normal _____

4 full _____

5 hello _____

6 none _____

manage	**remind**	**slice**	**report**
savage	**respond**	**spice**	**import**
package	**repent**	**notice**	**export**
postage	**record**	**police**	**forty**

☆ Learn the words, then use them to do the exercises.

☆ **WORD MAKER**   Use words from the list to complete the words below.

1 _ _ _ age   (untamed)

2 _ _ _ age   (to be in charge of)

3 _ _ _ _ age   (parcel)

4 re _ _ _ _ _   (a written account)

5 re _ _ _ _ _ _   (to answer)

6 re _ _ _ _ _   (to show remorse)

7 _ _ _ ice   (information about a future event)

8 _ _ ice   (a thin piece cut off something)

☆ **WORD HUNT**   Complete these sentences with words from the list.

1 My sister puts too much _____ in the food.

2 I spent £3 in _____ at the Post Office.

3 _____ me to pay the milkman in the morning.

4 Twenty and twenty make _____.

☆ **WORD HUNT**   Which words in the list have these smaller words inside them?

1 port _____, _____ and _____

2 cord _____

3 lice _____ and _____

☆ **WORD MATCH**   Find words in the list which mean the same as these words.

1 tell _____

2 fierce _____

3 answer _____

proper	damage	silent	prevent
property	voyage	parent	silence
consist	advantage	absent	remarkable
conduct	wages	serpent	blanket

☆ Learn the words, then use them to do the exercises.

☆ **WORD PUZZLE**   Use words from the list to complete the puzzle.

Clues down

1 to be composed (of)
2 thick bed covering
3 without noise
4 stop
6 possessions
8 not present
9 correct
10 earnings

Clues across

1 behaviour
3 absence of noise
5 snake
7 journey
9 father or mother
11 harm
12 superior power
13 striking

☆ **WORD MATCH**   Find words in the list which mean the same as these words.

1 journey _____

2 outstanding _____

3 stop _____

4 quietness _____

purple	former	also	murder
furnish	organ	almost	altogether
curtain	orchard	already	although
Saturday	coward	always	comfort

☆ Learn the words, then use them to do the exercises.

☆ **WORD PUZZLE**   Use the word 'altogether' to help form ten words from the list.

in addition

nearly

material drawn across a window

well-being

a keyboard instrument

unlawful killing

despite the fact that

a collection of fruit trees

before a stated time

a dark colour

☆ **EXPLANATIONS**   Complete these sentences with words from the list.

1 _____ is another way of saying 'forever'.

2 'Nearly' means the same as _____.

3 Someone who shows fear is a _____.

☆ **WORD HUNT**   Which words in the list have these smaller words inside them?

1 get _____

2 war _____

3 urn _____

4 hard _____

5 form _____

6 day _____

☆ **WORD MAKER**   Use words from the list to complete the words below.

1 al _ _   (too)

2 al _ _ _ _   (nearly)

3 al _ _ _ _   (forever)

harvest	perhaps	pitch	cargo
garment	permit	stitch	artist
alarm	perfect	kitchen	enjoy
farther	sermon	stretch	enjoyed

☆ Learn the words, then use them to do the exercises.

☆ **WORD PUZZLE**   Use words from the list to complete the puzzle.

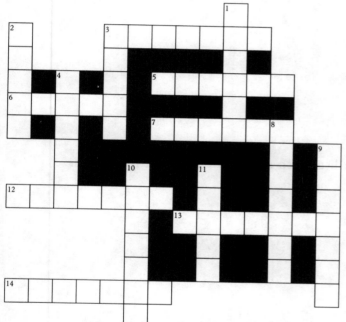

Clues down
1 allow
2 tar
3 take joy in
4 painter
8 gathering of crops
9 more distant
10 faultless
11 uneasiness

Clues across
3 took pleasure in
5 religious talk
6 load
7 sharp pain in the side
12 room where food is cooked
13 article of clothing
14 extend

☆ **WORD HUNT**   Which words in the list have these smaller words inside them?

1 vest _____

2 men _____

3 arm _____

4 far _____

5 car _____

6 art _____

☆ **SAYINGS**   Complete these sayings with words from the list.

1 A _____ in time saves nine.

2 Practice makes _____.

3 As black as _____.

tease	oven	linen	cheap
weave	woven	often	seam
preach	golden	hasten	eagle
beneath	dozen	listen	eager

☆ Learn the words, then use them to do the exercises.

☆ **WORD MAKER** Use words from the list to complete the words below.

1 _ _ en (device for baking food)

2 _ _ _ en (interlaced thread)

3 _ _ _ en (fabric made from flax)

4 _ _ _ en (twelve in number)

5 _ _ _ _ en (gold in colour)

6 ea _ _ _ (a large bird)

7 ea _ _ _ (impatient)

☆ **OPPOSITES** Find words in the list which mean the opposite of these words.

1 seldom _____

2 dawdle _____

3 above _____

4 expensive _____

5 reluctant _____

☆ **WORD HUNT** Which words in the list have these smaller words inside them?

1 we _____

2 each _____

3 as _____ and _____

4 am _____

☆ **WORD MATCH** Find words in the list which mean the same as these words.

1 hurry _____

2 inexpensive _____

3 under _____

4 keen _____

hotel	armour	intend	favourite
camel	parlour	inspect	bacon
label	colour	interest	apron
angel	favour	kingdom	grasp

☆ Learn the words, then use them to do the exercises.

☆ **WORD PUZZLE**   Use the word 'interest' to help form eight words from the list.

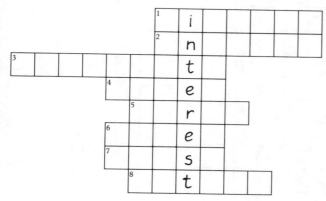

royal territory

examine closely

most liked

desert animal with hump

protective garment

identification card

seize

have in mind

☆ **WORD PUZZLE**   Use words from the list to complete the puzzle.

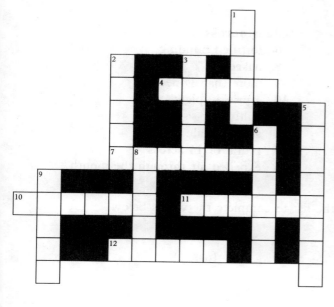

Clues down
1 place which provides meals and lodging
2 take hold of firmly
3 animal with hump
5 concern
6 defensive covering in battle
8 protective garment
9 cured flesh of the pig

Clues across
4 identification card
7 reception room
10 good will
11 tint
12 heavenly spirit

castle	grown	fare	human
thistle	blown	bare	woman
whistle	widow	dare	women
whisper	velvet	stare	spare

☆ Learn the words, then use them to do the exercises.

☆ **WORD PUZZLE** Use words from the list to complete the puzzle.

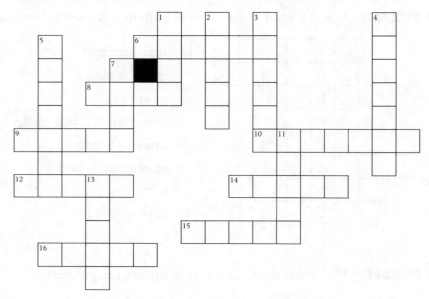

Clues down
1 charge for a journey
2 look fixedly
3 smooth, soft fabric
4 shrill sound
5 speak very softly
7 challenge
11 relating to mankind
13 woman whose husband has died

Clues across
6 fortified building
8 naked
9 more than is needed
10 a prickly plant
12 cultivated
14 adult female human
15 plural of 14 across
16 expelled air through the mouth

☆ **WORD MAKER** Use words from the list to complete the words below.

1 _ _ are (look intently)

2 _ _ are (something extra)

3 _ are (cost of travel)

4 _ are (defy)

5 _ are (naked)

stain	**explain**	**idle**	**fountain**
contain	**expect**	**island**	**mountain**
captain	**express**	**share**	**certain**
Britain	**extent**	**pantry**	**extra**

☆ Learn the words, then use them to do the exercises.

☆ **WORD MAKER**   Use words from the list to complete the words below.

1 _ tain   (discoloration)

2 _ _ _ tain   (person in charge of a vessel)

3 _ _ _ tain   (hold)

4 _ _ _ tain   (England, Wales & Scotland)

5 _ _ _ _ tain   (hill over 2,000 ft high)

6 _ _ _ _ tain   (natural spring of water)

7 _ _ _ tain   (sure)

8 ex _ _ _   (additional)

9 ex _ _ _ _   (anticipate)

10 ex _ _ _ _   (area)

11 ex _ _ _ _ _   (utter)

12 ex _ _ _ _ _ _   (give reasons for)

☆ **WORD HUNT**   Which words in the list have these smaller words inside them?

1 on   _____   5 press _____

2 cap _____   6 tent   _____

3 try   _____   7 is   _____

4 plain _____   8 hare   _____

☆ **WORD HUNT**   Find words in the list which mean the same as these words.

1 lazy   _____   4 hold   _____

2 sure   _____   5 surplus _____

3 divide _____   6 say   _____

paddle	playmate	hoof	settle
meddle	newspaper	smooth	midday
middle	platform	stoop	midnight
cripple	fortnight	stooped	choose

☆ Learn the words, then use them to do the exercises.

☆ **WORD MAKER**   Use words from the list to complete the words below.

1   _ oo _   (horny foot of certain animals)

2   _ _ oo _   (to bend)

3   _ _ oo _ _ _   (bent)

4   _ _ oo _ _   (pick)

5   _ _ oo _ _   (unruffled)

6   _ _ _ _ _ le   (to interfere)

7   _ _ _ _ _ le   (centre)

8   _ _ _ _ _ le   (to rest)

☆ **WORD PUZZLE**   Use the word 'fortnight' to help form nine words from the list.

1 f	foot of a horse
2 o	bend forward
3 r	lame person
4 t	come to rest
5 n	daily or weekly publication
6 i	noon
7 g	middle of the night
8 h	select
9 t	raised floor or stage

☆ **WORD HUNT**   Which words in the list have these smaller words inside them?

1   fort _____   4   new _____

2   form _____   5   rip _____

3   pad _____   6   mat _____

draper	county	limit	Wales
grate	country	spirit	Scotland
scale	cousin	timid	England
escape	message	public	English

☆ Learn the words, then use them to do the exercises.

☆ **WORD PUZZLE**   Use words from the list to complete the puzzle.

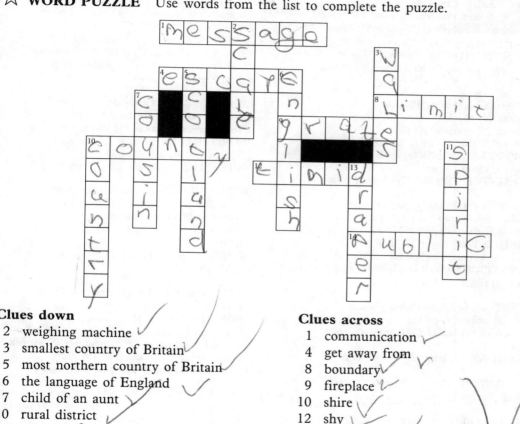

Clues down

2 weighing machine
3 smallest country of Britain
5 most northern country of Britain
6 the language of England
7 child of an aunt
10 rural district
11 ghost
13 dealer in fabrics

Clues across

1 communication
4 get away from
8 boundary
9 fireplace
10 shire
12 shy
14 open to all

☆ **WORD HUNT**   Which words in the list have these smaller words inside them?

1 rat   grate
2 is   english
3 in   cousin
4 cap   escape
5 age   message
6 rap   draper
7 try   country
8 gland   England
9 ale   scale   and   wales

Answers

2 WORD MAKER (1) slave (2) grave (3) shave
(4) gleam (5) treat (6) front (7) month
(8) wonder (9) Monday
WORD PUZZLE (1) won (2) ton (3) month
(4) Monday (5) cape (6) scream
WORD HUNT (1) cape, shape (2) team, steam
WORD MATCH (1) scream (2) gleam (3) won

3 WORD PUZZLE **Clues down** (1) joke
(2) pray (5) flutter (6) rode (8) plays (10) globe
Clues across (2) playing (3) poker (4) offer
(7) upper (9) saying (11) close (12) suffer
WORD HUNT (1) offer (2) close (3) pray
(4) globe (5) rode (6) flutter (7) sudden (8) plays
(9) staying

4 WORD HUNT (1) noise (2) peal
(3) thunder (4) shock (5) faint (6) struck
(7) moment (8) rainbow (9) plain
EXPLANATIONS (1) swift (2) struck (3) stuck
MINI PUZZLE (1) burst (2) spoil
(3) obtain (4) vain (5) soil
WORD MATCH (1) swift (2) struck (3) vain

5 WORD HUNT (1) money, pocket, silver
(2) needle, sew, button (3) sight, print
(4) high (5) sigh (6) honey (7) stockings
WORD HUNT (1) fright (2) fight
(3) stockings (4) needle (5) sight (6) button
EXPLANATIONS (1) sight (2) might
(3) fight (4) fright (5) light

6 WORD PUZZLE **Clues down** (1) leap
(2) deal (3) rabbit (4) robber
Clues across (1) ladder (5) bottom (6) spite
(7) wear
WORD HUNT (1) bear (2) tear (3) pear
(4) wear
WORD MATCH (1) real (2) pride (3) steal
(4) proud (5) rage

7 WORD PUZZLE (1) princess (2) music
(3) crown (4) begin (5) prince (6) main (7) gain
WORD HUNT (1) bringing (2) blowing
(3) begun (4) feeling (5) state (6) lord
(7) crown (8) music
EXPLANATIONS (1) begun (2) crowd (3) state
(4) gain (5) music

8 WORD PUZZLE (1) field (2) turnip (3) pea
(4) sow (5) vine (6) wine (7) grain
WORD HUNT (1) grain (2) drawing
(3) remain (4) grape (5) turnip (6) claw
(7) wheat (8) depart (9) travel (10) straw
(11) drawing, wine
WORD MAKER (1) claw (2) straw
(3) drawing (4) return (5) remain

9 WORD PUZZLE (1) pardon (2) donkey
(3) tide (4) monkey (5) swan (6) lion
EXPLANATIONS (1) forgive (2) prison
(3) polite (4) coast, shore (5) rude
WORD HUNT (1) animal, swan (2) prison,
punish (3) forgive, port, shore
WORD HUNT (1) prison (2) swan (3) port

10 WORD MAKER (1) owl (2) arrow
(3) growl (4) narrow (5) yellow (6) borrow
(7) pillow (8) sorrow
WORD PUZZLE (1) crust (2) gather
(3) path (4) chicken (5) enter (6) understood
WORD HUNT (1) rather, gather, path
(2) understand (3) crust

11 WORD PUZZLE **Clues down** (2) shake
(3) anger (4) trade (5) wade (7) sash
Clues across (1) moss (6) hunger (8) drank
WORD HUNT (1) carpet (2) hungry
(3) stream (4) splash (5) snake
OPPOSITES (1) danger (2) shallow (3) pale

12 WORD PUZZLE (1) stable (2) someone
(3) tumble (4) something (5) trust (6) April
(7) marble (8) charge (9) strange
WORD HUNT (1) sometimes (2) May (3) a
(4) large
WORD HUNT (1) form, thorn (2) stranger
(3) March

13 WEATHER WORDS (1) dusty (2) frosty
(3) cloudy (4) stormy
WORD HUNT (1) Thursday (2) unless
(3) happen (4) anybody (5) nobody (6) Friday
(7) Sunday (8) dusty (9) Thursday (10) happen
WORD HUNT (1) sport, sort, stormy
(2) unless (3) happen (4) handle (5) candle

14 WORD HUNT (1) crumb (2) thumb
(3) busy (4) glove (5) none (6) become (7) cover
(8) lucky (9) shelter (10) steady
OPPOSITES (1) dirty (2) busy (3) sleepy
(4) lucky (5) steady (6) climb
WORD HUNT (1) climb, lamb, comb, crumb,
thumb (2) stove, glove, none, become
WORD HUNT (1) lucky (2) crumb (3) shelter

15 WORD MAKER (1) brow (2) power
(3) towel (4) tower (5) shower (6) roll
(7) rolled (8) pulled (9) rolling
WORD PUZZLE (1) act (2) roll (3) tower
(4) chest (5) heart (6) pudding (7) cheek
WORD HUNT (1) brain (2) cottage (3) shower

16 WORD MAKER (1) snatch (2) catch (3) match
(4) patch (5) watch (6) fetch (7) ditch

WORD PUZZLE **Clues down** (1) July
(2) November (3) fetch
Clues across (1) June (4) everyone
(5) watch (6) reached
WORD HUNT (1) September, November
(2) picked, picking (3) learned

17 WORD PUZZLE (1) cradle (2) beak
(3) purse (4) darling (5) infant (6) nurse
(7) gentle
OPPOSITES (1) weak (2) dull (3) tender
(4) young (5) useless (6) careless
WORD MATCH (1) darling (2) young
(3) weak (4) dull
WORD HUNT (1) cradle (2) nurse (3) fur
(4) tender

18 WORD PUZZLE **Clues down** (1) tool
(2) cheese (6) too (7) geese (9) lunch
(10) blade (11) buy
Clues across (3) blood (4) cloth (5) stool
(7) goose (8) fool (10) beef (11) bench
(12) hammer
WORD HUNT (1) cloth (2) geese (3) blade,
blood (4) wire

19 WORD PUZZLE (1) broke (2) brighter
(3) miner (4) change (5) changed (6) taken
(7) broken (8) stole (9) eaten
WORD HUNT (1) cooler (2) brightest (3)
deeper (4) safer, safest (5) brighter, brightest
OPPOSITES (1) finer (2) break
(3) brighter (4) cooler (5) broke (6) deeper
(7) taken (8) safer

20 WORD PUZZLE **Clues down** (2) thief
(4) darkness (5) grief (6) shining (7) smiling
(8) cheer (10) skate
Clues across (1) burnt (3) hiding (8) chief
(9) illness (11) skating
WORD MATCH (1) nearly (2) quickly
(3) grief (4) illness (5) cheer (6) burnt
WORD HUNT (1) should (2) shining (3) thief

21 WORD PUZZLES (1) writing (2) repeat
(3) move (4) poem (5) prove (6) write
(7) remove (8) repair (9) Christmas (10) poet
(11) wrote (12) wrap
WORD HUNT (1) remark (2) Christmas
(3) clay (4) gray (5) repeat (6) wrote
WORD HUNT (1) wrap (2) remove (3) repeat

22 WORD PUZZLE **Clues down**
(1) grandmother (2) aloud (3) around (4) alike
(5) roam (7) cloak
Clues across (3) above (4) afraid (6) usual
(8) yesterday

WORD MIX-UP (1) afternoon (2) however
(3) breakfast
WORD MAKER (1) roam (2) coal (3) cloak
(4) float

23 WORD PUZZLE **Clues down**
(2) afterwards (3) forward (4) border (5) glasses
(8) inches (9) worth (11) branches
Clues across (1) starve (6) towards
(7) classes (10) order (11) branch (12) husband
(13) together (14) peaches
MORE THAN ONE (1) branches
(2) peaches (3) inches (4) glasses (5) classes

24 WORD PUZZLE **Clues down** (2) twice
(3) since (4) pepper (6) hurry (9) cuff
(10) birth (13) fir
Clues across (1) bitter (4) price (5) copper
(7) stuff (8) fence (11) silly (12) stiff
(14) birthday
OPPOSITES (1) silly (2) hurry (3) stiff
(4) bitter
WORD HUNT (1) bitter (2) pepper (3) visit

25 WORD PUZZLE **Clues down**
(2) wool (3) lemon (4) boxes (5) pretend
(7) sugar (9) track
Clues across (1) dwell (4) bloom
(8) present (10) quiet (11) dishes
EXPLANATIONS (1) friend (2) lemon
(3) flesh (4) forest (5) finger

26 WORD MAKER (1) fourth (2) fifth (3) tenth
WORD PUZZLE (1) person (2) cling
(3) term (4) twelve (5) serve (6) hundred
WORD HUNT (1) eleven (2) four (3) pint
(4) gift (5) upset
WORD MATCH (1) strip (2) upset
(3) simple (4) gift

27 WORD MAKER (1) voice (2) grace
(3) space (4) chance (5) earn (6) earth
WORD HUNT (1) daisies, lilies (2) bravely
(3) invite (4) voice (5) soap, soak
WORD PUZZLE (1) daisy (2) soak (3) lily
(4) soap (5) wise (6) earn (7) spider

28 NUMBER WORDS (a) thirty (b) thirteen
(c) fifty (d) sixteen (e) fourteen (f) twenty
(g) sixty (h) fifteen
WORD MAKER (1) wheel (2) between
(3) steep (4) creeping (5) deed (6) indeed
WORD HUNT (1) fourteen (2) between
(3) thousand (4) steel, wheel (5) deed
(6) thousand (7) sixteen (8) twenty

Mike 13
Jim 10
Mary

29 WORD PUZZLE (1) threw (2) half
(3) grind (4) crew (5) leaves (6) shelf (7) halves
MORE THAN ONE (1) loaves (2) thieves
(3) halves (4) leaves (5) themselves
WORD HUNT (1) chew (2) flew (3) shelf
(4) thrown (5) crew (6) loaf (7) themselves
(8) thieves

30 WORD PUZZLE **Clues down**
(1) knot (2) knife (3) finish (4) knives
(5) mail (7) snail
Clues across (1) knock (3) flock (6) wives
(8) tied (9) jail
WORD HUNT (1) Rail (2) knee (3) fixed
PAIRS (1) wives (2) tie (3) knife

31 WORD PUZZLE **Clues down**
(1) trunk (2) heaven (3) cure (4) paid
Clues across (3) capture (4) pure (5) lying
(6) deaf
OPPOSITES (1) raise (2) sure (3) defend
(4) raised
WORD MATCH (1) strike (2) dread
(3) picture (4) dying (5) sure (6) raise

32 WORD PUZZLE **Clues down**
(1) scrape (2) rattle (3) built (4) kettle
(5) content (8) build (9) tired (10) rate
Clues across (1) sore (6) cattle (7) cork
(8) bottle (11) flame (12) frame (13) battle
WORD HUNT (1) rate (2) tired (3) building
WORD HUNT (1) cattle (2) rattle (3) tired

33 WORD PUZZLE **Clues down** (1) answer
(2) swimming (3) butterfly (6) army
(10) shy (11) rank
Clues across (2) scout (4) shout (5) slipped
(6) axe (7) toe (8) manner (9) matter (10) spy
(12) flying (13) trying
WORD MATCH (1) shy (2) shout
(3) matter (4) answer (5) manner

34 WORD PUZZLE (1) starch (2) merrily
(3) arch (4) heavier (5) being (6) easiest
(7) because (8) touch
WORD HUNT (1) shadow (2) heavy
(3) heavier (4) heaviest
OPPOSITES (1) war (2) instant (3) easily
(4) heavy (5) cause (6) easier
WORD HUNT (1) shadow (2) starch
(3) instant (4) cause, because

35 WORD PUZZLE **Clues down**
(1) glory (2) mast (4) empty (5) history
(6) waste (7) good-bye (10) taste (11) loss
(15) lose
Clues across (3) fasten (8) past
(9) pity (12) copy (13) odd (14) plenty
(16) haste

OPPOSITES (1) lose (2) past (3) odd
(4) empty (5) good-bye (6) plenty

36 WORD MAKER (1) savage (2) manage
(3) package (4) record (5) respond (6) repent
(7) notice (8) slice
WORD HUNT (1) spice (2) postage
(3) Remind (4) forty
WORD HUNT (1) report, export, import
(2) record (3) slice, police
WORD MATCH (1) report (2) savage
(3) respond

37 WORD PUZZLE **Clues down**
(1) consist (2) blanket (3) silent (4) prevent
(6) property (8) absent (9) proper (10) wages
Clues across (1) conduct (3) silence
(5) serpent (7) voyage (9) parent (11) damage
(12) advantage (13) remarkable
WORD MATCH (1) voyage (2) remarkable
(3) prevent (4) silence

38 WORD PUZZLE (1) also (2) almost
(3) curtain (4) comfort (5) organ (6) murder
(7) although (8) orchard (9) already (10) purple
EXPLANATIONS (1) Always (2) almost
(3) coward
WORD HUNT (1) altogether (2) coward
(3) furnish (4) orchard (5) former (6) Saturday
WORD MAKER (1) also (2) almost (3) always

39 WORD PUZZLE **Clues down**
(1) permit (2) pitch (3) enjoy (4) artist
(8) harvest (9) farther (10) perfect (11) alarm
Clues across (3) enjoyed (5) sermon
(6) cargo (7) stitch (12) kitchen
(13) garment (14) stretch
WORD HUNT (1) harvest (2) garment
(3) alarm (4) farther (5) cargo (6) artist
SAYINGS (1) stitch (2) perfect (3) pitch

40 WORD MAKER (1) oven (2) woven
(3) linen (4) dozen (5) golden (6) eagle (7) eager
OPPOSITES (1) often (2) hasten (3) beneath
(4) cheap (5) eager
WORD HUNT (1) weave (2) preach (3) hasten,
tease (4) seam
WORD MATCH (1) hasten (2) cheap
(3) beneath (4) eager

41 WORD PUZZLE (1) kingdom (2) inspect
(3) favourite (4) camel (5) apron (6) label
(7) grasp (8) intend
WORD PUZZLE **Clues down**
(1) hotel (2) grasp (3) camel (5) interest
(6) armour (8) apron (9) bacon
Clues across (4) label (7) parlour
(10) favour (11) colour (12) angel